38

JOHNNY BRAVO in GOOD EATS

PERFECTION **46**

GRIM & EVIL in CENTRAL JUNCTION WHATS YOUR FUNCTION

54

£6.99

AH, SCHOOL.

VACATION IS ALMOST OVER AND SOON I WILL BE BACK IN MY *FAVORITE PLACES!*

THE *STUDY HALL.*

THE *LIBRARY.*

THE *GYM.*

BUT BEST OF ALL...

THE *SCIENCE LAB!*

OF COURSE IT DOES NOT COMPARE TO MY *LABORATORY...*

BUT HOW CAN I LOOK DOWN ON ANY *INCUBATOR* OF *DISCOVERY?*

UNLESS IT IS *FILTHY!*

IT'S OKAY, ANY JANITOR CAN MISS A SPOT--

OR TWO.

OR *THREE?*

NEAT FREAKED

THIS IS AN *OUTRAGE!* YOU CAN'T *TEACH SCIENCE* IN A *SEWER!*

JAMES DENNING- WRITER
MATT JENKINS- PENCILS
GARY FIELDS- INKS
RYAN CLINE- LETTERER
ZYLONOL- COLORIST
HARVEY RICHARDS- ASST. EDITOR
JOAN HILTY- EDITOR
DEXTER'S LABORATORY CREATED BY
GENNDY TARTAKOVSKY

SCHOOL OPENS IN ONLY 22 HOURS, AND IT WOULD TAKE AN *ARMY OF ROBOTS* TO CLEAN THIS PLACE UP! WHERE IN THE WORLD WOULD I FIND...

OH, RIGHT.

THE END

ROCK, GIRLS, ROCK!

ABBY DENSON—*writer*
BILL ALGER—*penciller*
MIKE DeCARLO—*inker*
JENNA GARCIA—*letterer*
DAVE TANGUAY—*colorist*
HARVEY RICHARDS—*asst. editor*
JOAN HILTY—*editor*

POWERPUFF GIRLS created by
CRAIG McCRACKEN

THE POWERPUFF GIRLS 37. June, 2003. Published monthly by DC Comics, 1700 Broadway, New York, NY 10019. POSTMASTER: Send address changes to THE POWERPUFF GIRLS, DC Comics Subscriptions, P.O. Box 0528, Baldwin, NY 11510. Annual subscription rate (12 issues) $27.00. Canadian subscribers must add $12.00 for postage and GST. GST # is R125921072. All foreign countries must add $12.00 for postage. U.S. funds only. Copyright©2003 Cartoon Network. All Rights Reserved. CARTOON NETWORK, the logo, POWERPUFF GIRLS and all related characters and elements are trademarks of and © Cartoon Network. The stories, characters and incidents mentioned in this magazine are entirely fictional. Printed on recyclable paper. DC Comics does not read or accept unsolicited submissions of ideas, stories or artwork.
Printed in Canada.
DC Comics. A division of Warner Bros.—An AOL Time Warner Company

AND SO, THE VERY NEXT DAY...

CALLING ALL MUSICIANS to the BATTLE OF THE BANDS! FIRST PRIZE THE KEY TO TOWNSVIL

HEY GUYS, LOOK AT THIS! THE WINNING ACT GETS THE *KEY TO TOWNSVILLE!*

WHAT'SSSS *THAT* DO?

I BET IT UNLOCKS EVERY DOOR IN TOWNSVILLE--WHICH MEANS WE COULD *STEAL* WHATEVER WE WANT WITH IT!

BOYS, WE'RE GONNA *ENTER THAT CONTEST!*

BUT BIG BILLY DON'T KNOW HOW TO PLAY ANY INSTRUMENTS!

PPPPLLLBBTTT!

ME NEITHER!

WE CAN BE ONE OF THOSE *BOY BANDS!* WE'LL JUST *SING* AND *DANCE*--

--AND JUST TO MAKE SURE WE *WIN*, WE'LL *SABOTAGE* THE OTHER BANDS' STUFF!

HA HA HA HA

CHECK OUT THE LATEST BOY BAND SENSATION...

4evRGreen!

OOH, A NEW BOY BAND! THEY'RE *DREAMY!*

BUBBLES, YOU DUMMY. THAT'S THE *GANGREEN GANG!*

I GUESS THEY WANT TO ENTER THAT BIG *BATTLE OF THE BANDS!*

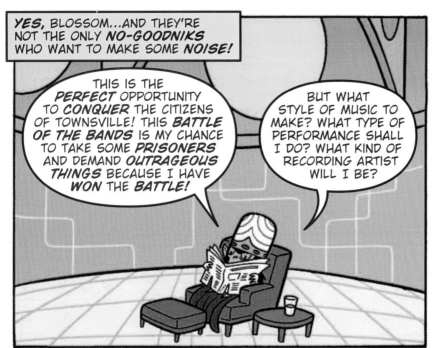

YES, BLOSSOM...AND THEY'RE NOT THE ONLY *NO-GOODNIKS* WHO WANT TO MAKE SOME *NOISE!*

THIS IS THE *PERFECT* OPPORTUNITY TO *CONQUER* THE CITIZENS OF TOWNSVILLE! THIS *BATTLE OF THE BANDS* IS MY CHANCE TO TAKE SOME *PRISONERS* AND DEMAND *OUTRAGEOUS THINGS* BECAUSE I HAVE *WON* THE *BATTLE!*

BUT WHAT STYLE OF MUSIC TO MAKE? WHAT TYPE OF PERFORMANCE SHALL I DO? WHAT KIND OF RECORDING ARTIST WILL I BE?

HMMM...

I SHALL BE A *DJ!* THIS *TURNTABLE* WILL BE PLACED INTO A *LARGER* DEVICE WHERIN I CAN HIDE *THREATENING WEAPONS* WITH WHICH I SHALL *THREATEN* THE *CITIZENS!*

THEY WILL BE CAPTIVATED BY MY *POWERFUL PERFORMANCE*, AND THEN (MORE LITERALLY) BY MY *POWERFUL WEAPONRY!*

MMM...I COULD ALSO BUILD IN SOME STROBE LIGHTS FOR THAT *EXTRA-FLASHY* EFFECT.

I DIDN'T KNOW MOJO WAS A MUSICIAN!

THIS IS STARTING TO LOOK MIGHTY *SUSPICIOUS.*

DJ MOJO'S BEATS WILL ROCK YOUR SOCKS AROUND THE BLOCK, BY WHICH I MEAN TO SAY YOU WILL BE MOVED TO THE GROOVE OF HIS TUNE. BLAH, BLAH...BLAH. BLAH.

WE OUGHTA NIP THIS IN THE BUD WITH SOME OLD-FASHIONED *BUTT-KICKING!*

24

LOOKS LIKE THE GIRLS ARE *ROCKING OUT* FOR JUSTICE!

WE'RE GONNA RISE ABOVE IT ALL! WHOAH! WHOAH! WHOAH!

GIRLS! WHAT IS THIS *RACKET?* I'M TRYING TO *WORK!*

BUT PROFESSOR--WE HAVE TO PRACTICE SO WE CAN WIN THE *BATTLE OF THE BANDS* SO THE *GANGREEN GANG* AND *MOJO JOJO* WON'T WIN!

YEAH!

PROFESSOR, IT REALLY *IS* FOR CRIME-FIGHTING PURPOSES. WE'LL TRY TO KEEP IT DOWN.

WELL...-»SIGH«- OKAY. JUST TRY TO GIVE ME SOME *WARNING* NEXT TIME!

26

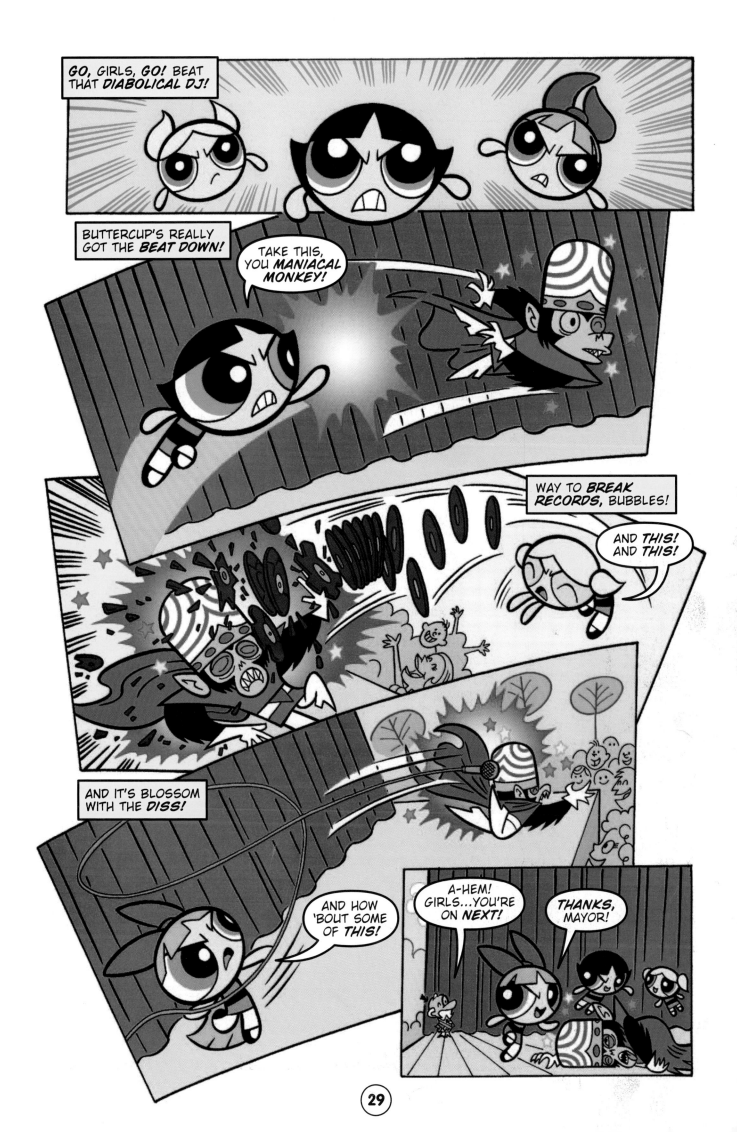

WRITER- **MICHAEL KRAIGER**
PENCILLER- **VINCENT DEPORTER**
INKER- **ANGUS BUNGAY**
COLORIST- **DIGITAL CHAMELEON**
LETTERS- **RYAN CLINE**
EDITOR- **JOAN HILTY**
ASST EDITOR- **HARVEY RICHARDS**
ED, EDD, and EDDY created by
DANNY ANTONUCCI

CARTOON CARTOONS 2. April, 2001. Published monthly by DC Comics, 1700 Broadway, New York, NY 10019. POSTMASTER: Send address changes to CARTOON CARTOONS, DC Comics Subscriptions, P.O. Box 0528, Baldwin, NY 11510. Annual subscription rate $23.88. Canadian subscribers must add $12.00 for postage and GST. GST # is R125921072. All foreign countries must add $12.00 for postage. U.S. funds only. Copyright © 2001 Cartoon Network. All Rights Reserved. CARTOON NETWORK, the logo, and all characters and elements depicted herein are trademarks of Cartoon Network. The stories, characters and incidents mentioned in this magazine are entirely fictional. Printed on recyclable paper. Printed in Canada.
DC Comics. A division of Warner Bros.—A Time Warner Entertainment Company

I AM THE GHOST OF DAY-OLD BREAD!

WHIRRrrTHUPrrBLUNKrrBLurp!

WHIRRrrTHUPrrBLUNKrrBLurp!

I THINK WE NEED A BIGGER BOWL!

UH, DOUBLE DEE, HOW 'BOUT A HAND HERE?

NOT GOOD, NOT GOOD...

THIS REMINDS ME OF "MUCUS MONSTER FROM BEYOND THE HOLE"!

SHUT... UP...ED!

WILL THEY SURVIVE ITS WRATH?

NO ONE WILL SURVIVE IF MOTHER SEES THIS MESS! OH DEAR!

THE END

FRANK STROM——————Writer
GARY TERRY——————Penciller
SCOTT McRAE——————Inker
JENNA GARCIA——————Letterer
DIGITAL CHAMELEON——Colorist
HARVEY RICHARDS——Asst. Editor
JOAN HILTY——————Editor
JOHNNY BRAVO created by VAN PARTIBLE

AT LEAST I'LL GET A *DECENT MEAL* OUT OF THIS.

GOT IT *COVERED!* OL' JOHNNY'S TAKING YOU FOR A FANCY FEAST OF *INTERNATIONAL CUISINE...*

...*CORNDOGS* AND CURLY FRIES, TOPPED OFF WITH *ITALIAN ICE*-- THAT'S THE *INTERNATIONAL* PART!

WHA-A-AT?!?

LOUIE'S

HOT DOGS

LOSER!

HEY, WHERE YA GOIN'? THIS *CONTINENTAL CHOW* DON'T COME *CHEAP*, YA KNOW!

I DON'T GET IT, MAMA-- WHAT WENT *WRONG?* I THOUGHT CHICKS *LOVED* CORNDOGS!

THEY'RE CORNY *AND* BEEFY... LIKE *ME!*

OH, JOHNNY! YOU'LL *NEVER* WIN HER OVER LIKE *THAT!*

I'LL LET YOU IN ON A LI'L *SECRET*--

--*ALL* WOMEN ARE IMPRESSED BY MEN WHO CAN *COOK!*

REALLY? SEEMS TOO *SIMPLE*, BUT I GUESS YOU'D KNOW BEST!

UH...MAMA? IS THIS SUPPOSED TO BE *FISH* OR *JELLO?*

KEEP YER PAWS TO YOURSELF AND *STAY OUT!!*

BOOKSTORE

BIG COOKBOOK SALE

AH, WHO EVER LEARNED COOKIN' FROM A *BOOK,* ANYHOW? TOO MANY *BIG WORDS!*

KWANG!

BOOT!

I NEED AN *EXPERIENCED CHEF.* MAYBE POPS CAN...

DANG! I ONLY WANTED A *RECIPE* FOR *ROMANCE...!*

KEE-RASH

WHOA, MAMA! *SORRY* ABOUT THAT, MASTER HONG!

AS THE *ANCIENT PROVERB* SAYS, THE SWIFT *RABBIT* WHO FORGES ON WITHOUT *LOOKING...*

...IS AN *IDIOT!*

I'M JUST KINDA IN A HURRY TO *LEARN* SOMETHIN' *IMPORTANT...*

HEY! DID YOU JUST CALL ME A *"RABBIT"?!?*

HONG WILL TEACH YOU WHAT YOU NEED TO KNOW...IF IT GETS YOU OFF THE *SIDEWALK!*

NAH, YOU DON'T *GET* ME.

YOU'RE A *MARTIAL ARTS* INSTRUCTOR--I GOTTA LEARN TO *COOK,* NOT *FIGHT!*

THE ART OF *WAR* OFTEN BEGINS IN THE *KITCHEN!*

41

AND SO...

MY LITTLE JOHNNY--A MASTER CHEF! YOU DESERVE A REWARD, MASTER HONG!

THERE IS NO GREATER REWARD THAN A WELL-SCHOOLED PUPIL!

I STILL THINK HE'S A FRAUD!

SORRY, DARLIN'--FRAUD AIN'T ON THE MENU TONIGHT.

INSTEAD I GIVE YOU CHICKEN A LA BRAVO! DIG IN!

WOW! WHAT A MASTERPIECE!

MUNCH-MUNCH!

ALMOST LOOKS TOO GOOD TO EAT!

HEH-HEH. DON'T RUSH-- YOU'LL MISS THE SUBTLE FLAVORIN'!

GLEEP!

CHOKE!

AH-OO-GAH!

HUH! GUESS THEY DIDN'T MISS IT!

THE END

COW and CHICKEN

UDDER PERFECTION

DAN SLOTT-writer
TIM HARKINS-artist & letterer
DAVE TANGUAY-colors
HARVEY RICHARDS-assist
HEIDI MACDONALD-edits

COW and CHICKEN
created by
DAVID FEISS

CARTOON NETWORK STARRING 7. March, 2000. Published monthly by DC Comics, 1700 Broadway, New York, NY 10019. POSTMASTER: Send address changes to CARTOON NETWORK STARRING, DC Comics Subscriptions, P.O. Box 0528, Baldwin, NY 11510. Annual subscription rate $23.88. Canadian subscribers must add $12.00 for postage and GST. GST # is R125921072. All foreign countries must add $12.00 for postage. U.S. funds only. Copyright © 2000 Cartoon Network. All Rights Reserved. Cow and Chicken and all related characters and elements depicted herein are trademarks of Cartoon Network. Cartoon Network ® and Cartoon Network logo are trademarks of Cartoon Network. The stories, characters and incidents mentioned in this magazine are entirely fictional. Printed in Canada.
Printed on recyclable paper.
DC Comics. A division of Warner Bros.–A Time Warner Entertainment Company

PLASTIC SURGEON

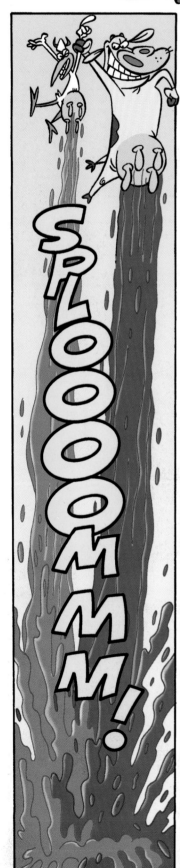

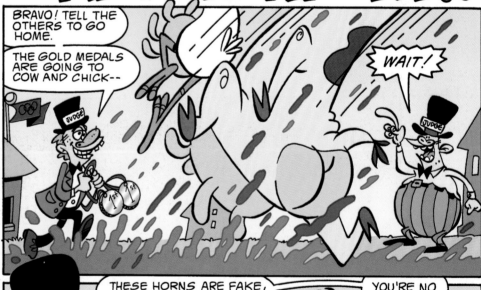

CARTOON CARTOONS 14. January, 2003. Published bimonthly by DC Comics, 1700 Broadway, New York, NY 10019. POSTMASTER: Send address changes to CARTOON CARTOONS, DC Comics Subscriptions, P.O. Box 0528, Baldwin, NY 11510. Annual subscription rate $13.50. Canadian subscribers must add $6.00 for postage and GST. GST # is R125921072. All foreign countries must add $6.00 for postage. U.S. funds only. Copyright © 2003 Cartoon Network. All Rights Reserved. CARTOON NETWORK, the logo, and all characters and elements depicted herein are trademarks of Cartoon Network. The stories, characters and incidents mentioned in this magazine are entirely fictional. Printed on recyclable paper. DC Comics does not read or accept unsolicited submissions of ideas, stories or artwork.
Printed in Canada.

DC Comics. A division of Warner Bros.—An AOL Time Warner Company

• JENETTE KAHN, President & Editor-in-Chief • PAUL LEVITZ, Executive Vice President & Publisher • MIKE CARLIN, VP-Executive Editor •
• JOAN HILTY, Editor • HARVEY RICHARDS, Assistant Editor • GEORG BREWER, VP-Design & Retail Product Development • RICHARD BRUNING, VP-Creative Director •
PATRICK CALDON, Senior VP-Finance & Operations • TERRI CUNNINGHAM, VP-Managing Editor • DAN DIDIO, VP-Editorial • JOEL EHRLICH, Senior VP Advertising & Promotions •
ALISON GILL, VP-Manufacturing • LILLIAN LASERSON, VP & General Counsel • JIM LEE, Editorial Director-WildStorm • DAVID McKILLIPS, VP-Advertising •
• JOHN NEE, VP-Business Development • CHERYL RUBIN, VP-Licensing & Merchandising • BOB WAYNE, VP-Sales & Marketing •

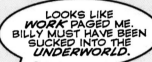

...TOO LATE.

GOOD EVENING, FOLKS, AND WELCOME TO THE AFTERLIFE. I'M *JIM*, YOUR TOUR GUIDE ON YOUR TRIP TO YOUR *FINAL DESTINATION!*

LATER...

AND YOU'LL SEE THE *RIVER STYX* COMING UP ON YOUR RIGHT IN JUST A MOMENT...

WE'RE DOOMED.

OOOOH!

NORMALLY, I FIND ROAD TRIPS TO BE A BORE.

BUT THIS ONE IS ACTUALLY KIND OF *INTERESTING.*

FOLKS, I'VE GOT GREAT NEWS. WE'LL BE STOPPING FOR SOMETHING TO EAT AT THE FAMOUS *DANTE'S INFERNO.*

FROM THERE— IT'S A *NONSTOP TRIP* TO YOUR *FINAL DESTINATION!*

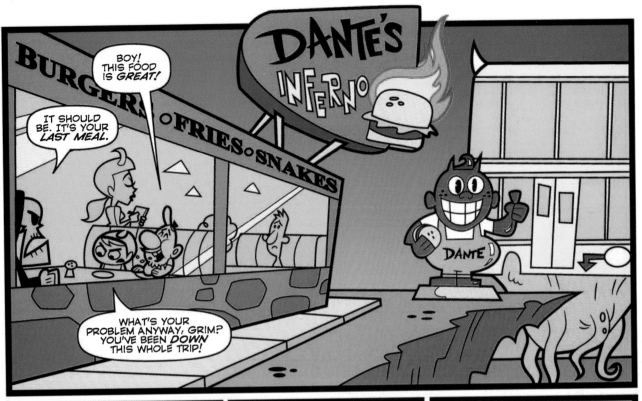